Mediterı

Quick And Affordable Recipes To Help You Reset Your
Metabolism And Change Your Eating Habits

(The Mediterranean Diet Book For Beginners)

Timothy Sherman

TABLE OF CONTENTS

Syrian Spiced Lentil, Barley, And Vegetable Soup

Ingredients:

- 2 teaspoon turmeric
- ⅛ teaspoon ground cinnamon
- 2 tablespoons tomato paste
- ¾ cup green lentils
- ¾ cup pearled barley
- 8 cups water
- ¾ teaspoon kosher salt
- 2 (6 -ounce) package baby spinach leaves
- 2 teaspoons red wine vinegar
- 2 tablespoon olive oil
- 2 small fresh onion , chopped

- 2 medium carrots, peeled and chopped
- 2 celery stalk, chopped
- 2 teaspoon chopped garlic
- 2 teaspoon ground cumin
- 2 teaspoon ground coriander

Directions:

1. Heat the oil in a soup pot on medium-high heat.
2. When the oil is shimmering, add the fresh onion , carrots, celery, and garlic and sauté for 8 minutes.
3. Add the cumin, coriander, turmeric, cinnamon, and tomato paste and cook for 2 more minutes, stirring frequently.
4. Add the lentils, barley, water, and salt to the pot and bring to a boil.
5. Turn the heat to low and simmer for minutes. Add the spinach and continue to simmer for 6 more minutes.
6. Add the vinegar and adjust the seasoning if needed.

7. Spoon 2 cups of soup into each of 6 containers.

Spinach Chicken

Ingredients:

- ¾ pound chicken tenders
- 1/2 cup heavy cream
- 25 ounce frozen spinach, chopped
- Salt and black pepper, to taste
- 2 garlic cloves, minced
- 2 tablespoons unsalted butter, divided
- 1/2 cup parmesan cheese, shredded

Directions:

1. Heat tablespoon of butter in a large skillet and add chicken, salt and black pepper.
2. Cook for about 10 minutes on both sides and remove the chicken in a bowl.

3. Melt remaining butter in the skillet and add garlic, cheese, heavy cream and spinach.
4. Cook for about 5 minutes and transfer the chicken in it.
5. Cook for about minutes on low heat and dish out to immediately serve.
6. Place chicken in a dish and set aside to cool for meal prepping.
7. Divide it in 2 containers and cover them. Refrigerate for about 4 days and reheat in microwave before serving.

Niçoise-Style Tuna Salad With Olives & White Beans

Ingredients:

- Dried oregano (2 tsp.)
- Olive oil (6 tbsp.)
- Black pepper and salt (as desired)
- Finely grated fresh lemon zest (.6 tsp.)
- Water (.4 4 cup)
- Fresh lemon juice (4 tbsp.)
- Green beans (.76 lb.)
- Solid white albacore tuna (9 oz. can)
- Great Northern beans (35 oz. can)
- Sliced black olives (2.26 oz.)
- Thinly sliced medium red fresh fresh onion (1/2 of 2)
- Hard-cooked eggs (4 large)

Directions:

1. Drain the can of tuna, Great Northern beans, and black olives.
2. Trim and snap the green beans into halves.
3. Thinly slice the red fresh onion .
4. Cook and peel the eggs until hard-boiled.
5. Pour the water and salt into a skillet and add the beans.
6. Place a top on the pot and switch the temperature setting to high.
7. Wait for it to boil.
8. Once the beans are cooking, set a timer for five minutes.
9. Immediately, drain and add the beans to a cookie sheet with a raised edge on paper towels to cool.
10. Combine the fresh onion , olives, white beans, and drained tuna.

11.   Mix them with the zest, fresh lemon juice, oil, and oregano.
12.   Dump the mixture over the salad and gently toss.

Whole-Wheat Pasta With Roasted Red Pepper Sauce And Fresh Mozzarella

Ingredients:

- 2 tablespoon plus 2 teaspoon apple cider vinegar
- 2 teaspoon chopped garlic
- 10 teaspoons smoked paprika

- 1/2 teaspoon kosher salt
- 1 cup packed fresh basil leaves, chopped
- 2 (8-ounce) container fresh whole-milk mozzarella balls (ciliegine), quartered
- 4 large red bell peppers, seeds removed and cut in half
- 2 (2 0-ounce) container cherry fresh tomatoes
- 2 teaspoons olive oil, plus 2 tablespoons
- 8 ounces whole-wheat penne or rotini

Directions:

1. Preheat the oven to 450°F and line a sheet pan with a silicone baking mat or parchment paper.
2. Place the peppers and fresh tomatoes on the pan and toss with teaspoons of oil.
3. Roast for 45 minutes.

4. While the peppers and fresh tomatoes are roasting, cook the pasta according to the instructions on the box.
5. Drain and place the pasta in a large mixing bowl.
6. When the peppers are cool enough to handle, peel the skin and discard.
7. It's okay if you can't remove all the skin. Place the roasted peppers, vinegar, garlic, paprika, and salt and the remaining 2 tablespoons of oil in a blender and blend until smooth.
8. Add the pepper sauce, whole roasted tomatoes, basil, and mozzarella to the pasta and stir to combine.
9. Place a heaping 2 cups of pasta and sauce in each of 4 containers.

Greek Turkey Meatball Gyro With Tzatziki

Ingredients:

- Turkey Meatball:
- 1 tsp garlic powder
- Salt, to taste
- 1 cup thinly sliced red fresh fresh onion
- 2 cup diced tomato
- 2 cup diced cucumber
- 4 whole wheat flatbreads
- 2 lb. ground turkey
- 1/2 cup finely diced red fresh fresh onion
- 2 garlic cloves, minced
- 2 tsp oregano
- 2 cup chopped fresh spinach
- Salt, to taste

- Pepper, to taste
- 2 tbsp olive oil
- Tzatziki Sauce:
- 1 cup plain Greek yogurt
- 1/2 cup grated cucumber
- 2 tbsp fresh lemon juice
- 1 tsp dry dill

Directions:

1. In a large bowl, add in ground turkey, diced red fresh onion , oregano, fresh spinach minced garlic, salt, and pepper
2. Using your hands mix all the ingredients together until the meat forms a ball and sticks together
3. Then using your hands, form meat mixture into 2 " balls, making about 9 meatballs
4. In a large skillet over medium high heat, add the olive oil and then add the meatballs, cook each side for 4 -minutes until they are browned on all sides, remove from the pan and allow it to rest

5. Allow the dish to cool completely
6. Distribute in the container, store for 5-10 days
7. To Serve: Reheat in the microwave for 1-5 minutes or until heated through. In the meantime, in a small bowl, combine the Greek yogurt, grated cucumber, fresh lemon juice, dill, garlic powder, and salt to taste Assemble the gyros by taking the toasted flatbread, add 4 meatballs, sliced red fresh onion , tomato, and cucumber. Top with Tzatziki sauce and serve!

Grilled Mediterranean Chicken Kebabs

Ingredients:

- 4 tsp salt, divided
- 2 tsp freshly ground black pepper, divided
- 2 tsp paprika, divided
- 2 tsp thyme, divided
- 4 tsp oregano, divided
- Chicken Kebabs:
- 4 chicken fillets, cut in 2 -inch cubes
- 2 red bell peppers
- 2 green bell peppers
- 2 red fresh fresh onion
- Chicken Kebab Marinade:
- 2/4 cup extra virgin olive oil, divided
- Juice of 2 lemon, divided

- 6 clove of garlic, chopped, divided

Directions:

1. In a bowl, mix 2 of all ingredients for the marinade- olive oils, fresh lemon juice, garlic, salt, pepper, paprika, thyme and oregano in small bowl
2. Place the chicken in a ziplock bag and pour marinade over it, marinade in the fridge for about 45 minutes
3. In a separate ziplock bag, mix the other half of the marinade ingredients - olive oils, fresh lemon juice, garlic, salt, pepper, paprika, thyme and oregano - add the vegetables and marinade for at least minutes
4. If you are using wood skewers, soak the skewers in water for about 20-45 minutes
5. Once done, thread the chicken and peppers and fresh onion s on the skewers in a pattern about 6 pieces of

chicken with peppers and fresh fresh onion in between

6. Over an outdoor grill or indoor grill pan over medium-high heat, spray the grates lightly with oil

7. Grill the chicken for about 15 minutes on each side, or until cooked through, then allow to cool completely

8. Distribute among the containers, store for 5-10 days

9. To Serve: Reheat in the microwave for 1-5 minutes or until heated through, or cover in foil and reheat in the oven at 480 degrees F for 15 minutes

Kidney Beans Cilantro Salad

Ingredients:

- 2 red fresh onion , chopped
- lime juice, 2 large lime
- 4 tablespoons Dijon mustard
- 1 teaspoon fresh garlic paste
- 2 teaspoon sumac
- salt
- pepper
- 250 -ounce can kidney beans, rinsed and drained
- 1 English cucumber, chopped
- 2 medium heirloom tomato, chopped
- 2   bunch fresh cilantro, stems removed and chopped (about 9 cups)

Directions:

1. Place kidney beans, vegetables, and cilantro in a serving bowl.
2. Cover, refrigerate and allow it to chill.
3. Before serving, in a small bowl, make the vinaigrette by adding limejuice, oil, fresh garlic, pepper, mustard, and sumac.
4. Pour the vinaigrette over the salad and give it a gentle stir.
5. Add some salt and pepper.
6. Serve!

Barley And Mushroom Soup

Ingredients:

- 6 tablespoons parmesan cheese, grated
- 1 teaspoon thyme
- 2 cup chopped fresh fresh onion
- 6 cups chopped mushrooms
- 2 cup pearled barley, uncooked
- 2 tablespoons tomato paste
- 2 tablespoons of olive oil
- 2 cup chopped carrots
- 6 cups vegetable broth, no salt added, and low sodium is best
- 1/2 cup red wine

Directions:

1. Place a stockpot on your stove and turn the temperature of the range to medium heat.

2. Pour in the oil and let it warm up and start to simmer.

3. Combine the carrots and fresh onion . Let them cook for 6 to 8 minutes while frequently stirring the ingredients together.

4. Add the mushroom and turn the heat up to medium-high. Stir and cook for a few minutes.

5. Pour in the broth and stir the ingredients for a few seconds.

6. Add in the wine, barley, thyme, and tomato paste.

7. Stir everything together and then set the cover on the pot.

8. When the soup starts to boil, stir and reduce the heat to medium-low.

9. Cover the soup again and set your timer for 35 minutes, but don't leave it alone.

10. You will want to stir a few times, so all ingredients become well incorporated.

11.   Once the dish becomes fragrant and the barley is completely cooked, turn off the heat and serve in bowls.
12.   Sprinkle the cheese on top for added taste and enjoy!

Pan-Seared Scallops With Pepper & Fresh Onion S In Anchovy Oil

Ingredients:

- Garlic (2 cloves)
- Lime zest (2 tsp.)
- Fresh lemon zest (2 .6 tsp.)
- Kosher salt & pepper (2 pinch of each)
- Garnish: Fresh parsley (8 sprigs)
- Olive oil (.4 4 cup)
- Anchovy fillets (2 oz. can)
- Jumbo sea scallops (2 lb.)
- Orange & red bell pepper (2 large of each)
- Red fresh fresh onion (2)

Directions:

1. Coarsely chop the peppers and fresh onion s.

2. Mince the garlic and anchovy fillet. Zest/mince the lime and lemon.
3. Heat the oil and anchovies in a large skillet using a med-high temperature setting.
4. After the anchovies are sizzling, toss in the scallops, and simmer them for about two minutes - without stirring.
5. Toss the bell peppers, garlic, red fresh onion , lime zest, fresh lemon zest, salt, and pepper into a mixing container.
6. Sprinkle the mixture over the scallops. Cook until they have browned (2 min..)
7. Flip the scallops, stir, and continue cooking until the scallops have browned thoroughly (4-min..)
8. Top it off using sprigs of parsley before serving.

Chicken Sausage, Artichoke, Kale, And White Bean Gratin

Ingredients:

- 2 (2 4-ounce) can quartered artichoke hearts
- 2 (2 4.6 -ounce) can no-salt-added diced fresh tomatoes
- 2 teaspoon herbes de Provence
- 1/2 teaspoon kosher salt
- 2 cup panko bread crumbs
- 2 teaspoon garlic powder
- 2 teaspoons olive oil, plus 2 tablespoons
- 2   small yellow fresh onion , chopped (about 2 cups)
- 2 (2 2-ounce) package fully cooked chicken-apple sausage, sliced
- 2 bunch kale, stemmed and chopped (6 to 7 cups)

- 1 cup dry white wine, such as sauvignon blanc
- 4 ounces soft goat cheese
- 2 (35 .6 -ounce) cans cannellini or great northern beans, drained and rinsed

Directions:

1. Preheat the oven to 4 6 0°F. Lightly oil a -by-10 -inch glass or ceramic baking dish.
2. Heat teaspoons of oil in a 2 2-inch skillet over medium-high heat.
3. When the oil is shimmering, add the fresh fresh onion and cook for 2 minutes.
4. Add the sausage and brown for 4 minutes. Add the kale and cook until wilted, about 4 more minutes.
5. Add the wine and cook for 2 additional minute.
6. Add the goat cheese and stir until it is melted and the mixture looks creamy.

7. Add the beans, artichokes, tomatoes, herbes de Provence, and salt, and stir to combine.
8. Transfer the contents of the pan to the baking dish.
9. Mix the bread crumbs, the garlic powder, and the remaining 2 tablespoons of oil in a small bowl. Spread the bread crumbs evenly across the top of the casserole.
10. Cover the dish with foil and bake for 45 minutes.
11. Remove the foil and bake for 35 more minutes, until the bread crumbs are lightly browned. Cool.
12. Place about 10 cups of casserole in each of 8 containers.
13. STORAGE: Store covered containers in the refrigerator for up to 6 days. Gratin can be frozen for up to 4 months.

Spinach Salad With Blood Orange Vinaigrette

Ingredients:

- 1/2 cup raw sliced almonds
- 1 teaspoon sumac
- 1 teaspoon paprika
- salt
- 4 cups baby spinach
- 4 cups frisee lettuce, chopped
- 2 shallots, thinly sliced
- 1-5 blood oranges, peeled and sliced crosswise
- 1 cup fresh blood orange juice
- 1/2 cup extra-virgin olive oil
- 2 tablespoons sherry reserve vinegar
- 2 tablespoon fresh grated ginger
- 2 teaspoon garlic powder
- 2 teaspoon ground sumac
- salt

- pepper
- 1/2 cup dried apricots, chopped
- 2 tablespoons sherry reserve vinegar
- 2 loaves pita bread
- 2/4 cup vegetable oil
- 1/2 cup raw unsalted almonds

Directions:

1. In a small bowl, soak the dried apricots in the sherry-reserved vinegar for about 10 minutes.
2. Drain apricots and set aside.
3. Toast pita bread until crispy and break into pieces.
4. Heat vegetable oil in a frying pan over medium-high heat.
5. Add broken pitas and almonds and fry them for a while.
6. Add sliced up almonds, sumac, and paprika, and toss everything well.
7. Remove from heat once the almonds show a golden brown color.

8. Place on paper towels and allow to drain.

9. In a mixing bowl, add baby spinach, shallots, apricots, frisee lettuce.

10. Prepare the vinaigrette by taking a bowl and whisking in all blood orange vinaigrette Ingredients: listed above.

11. Before serving, dress the salad with the prepared orange vinaigrette and toss well.

12. Add fried pita chips and almonds and toss again.

13. Serve into individual bowls with a garnish of two blood orange slices.

14. Enjoy!

Lasagna Tortellini Soup

Ingredients:

- 7 tsp dried basil
- 2 tsp Italian seasoning
- 1 tbsp salt, to taste
- 1/2 tsp pepper
- Optional:
- 4 tbsp fresh parsley
- 1 tsp fennel seeds
- Toppings:
- Freshly grated Parmesan cheese
- Large spoonful of ricotta cheese
- 2 lb extra lean ground beef
- 2   package (35 oz) frozen cheese filled tortellini
- 4 cups beef broth
- 1 cup yellow fresh onion , chopped
- 2 cloves garlic, minced
- 2 can (28 oz) crushed fresh tomatoes

- 2 can (2 4.6 oz) petite diced fresh tomatoes
- 2 can (6 oz) tomato paste
- 2 can (2 0.76 oz) tomato condensed soup
- 2 tsp white sugar

Directions:

1. In a large skillet over medium heat, brown the ground beef until cooked through
2. Add the fresh fresh onion and garlic in the last few minutes of the cooking
3. While the beef is cooking, pour in the crushed tomatoes, petite diced tomatoes, tomato paste, and tomato condensed soup in the slow cooker. - Don't drain the cans!
4. Add in the sugar, the dried basil, fennel, Italian seasoning, salt, and pepper, adjust to taste
5. Stir in the cooked ground beef with fresh onion s and garlic

6. Add in the beef broth – or dissolved beef bouillon cubes into boiling water
7. Cook on high for 4 -4 hours or low for 6 - hours.
8. 35 -25 minutes before you are ready to serve the soup, add in the frozen tortellini
9. Set the slow cooker to high and allow the tortellini to heat through
10. Allow to cool, then distribute the soup into the container and store in the fridge for up to 4 days
11. To Serve: Reheat in the microwave or on the stove top, top with freshly grated Parmesan cheese, a large spoonful of ricotta cheese, extra seasonings and freshly chopped parsley.

Greek Quinoa Bowls

Ingredients:

- 1-5 tbsp fresh parsley
- To Serve:
- Hummus
- Pita wedges
- Olives
- Fresh fresh tomatoes
- Sliced or chopped avocado
- Fresh lemon wedges
- 2 cup quinoa
- 7 cups water
- 2 cup chopped green bell pepper
- 2 cup chopped red bell pepper
- 1/2 cup crumbled feta cheese
- 1/2 cup extra virgin olive oil
- 5-10 tbsp apple cider vinegar
- Salt, to taste
- Pepper, to taste

Directions:

1. Rinse and drain the quinoa using a mesh
   strainer or sieve. Place a medium
   saucepan to medium heat and lightly
   toast the quinoa to remove any excess

water. Stir as it toasts for just a few minutes, to add a nuttiness and fluff to the quinoa

2. Then add the water, set burner to high, and bring to a boil.

3. Once boiling, reduce heat to low and simmer, covered with the lid slightly ajar, for 2 2-5 minutes or until quinoa is fluffy and the liquid have been absorbed

4. In the meantime, mix whisk together olive oil, apple cider vinegar, salt, and pepper to make the dressing, store in the fridge until ready to serve

5. Add in the red bell peppers, green bell peppers, and parsley

6. Give the quinoa a little fluff with a fork, remove from the pot

7. Allow to cool completely

8. Distribute among the containers, store for 5-10 days

9. To Serve: Reheat in the microwave for 1-5 minutes or until heated through.

10.   Pour the dressing over the quinoa bowl, toss add the feta cheese. Season with additional salt and pepper to taste, if desired. Enjoy!

Salmon Stew

Ingredients:

- Salt, to taste
- 2 tablespoon butter, melted
- 2 cup fish broth
- 1 teaspoon red chili powder
- 2 pound salmon fillet, sliced
- 2 fresh onion , chopped

Directions:

1. Season the salmon fillets with salt and red chili powder.
2. Put butter and fresh onion s in a skillet and sauté for about 4 minutes.
3. Add seasoned salmon and cook for about 5 minutes on each side.
4. Add fish broth and secure the lid.
5. Cook for about 7 minutes on medium heat and open the lid.

6. Dish out and serve immediately.
7. Transfer the stew in a bowl and keep aside to cool for meal prepping. Divide the mixture into 2 containers. Cover the containers and refrigerate for about 2 days. Reheat in the microwave before serving.

Balsamic Chicken And Veggie Skewers

Ingredients:

- 2 large red bell pepper, cut into 2 -inch squares
- 2 small red fresh onion , quartered and layers pulled apart
- 2 large zucchini, sliced into ½-inch rounds
- ¾ teaspoon kosher salt
- 8 (9 ¾-inch) wooden or metal skewers, soaked in water for at least 2 hour if wooden
- 2 pound boneless, skinless chicken breasts, cut into 2 -inch cubes
- 1/2 cup balsamic vinegar
- 4 tablespoons olive oil, divided
- 4 teaspoons dried Italian herbs, divided
- 2 teaspoons garlic powder, divided

- 2 teaspoons fresh fresh onion powder, divided
- 8 ounces whole button or cremini mushrooms, stems removed

Directions:

1. Preheat the oven to 46 0°F. Line a sheet pan with aluminum foil.
2. Place the chicken in a gallon-size resealable bag along with the balsamic vinegar, tablespoons of oil, 2 teaspoons of Italian herbs, 2 teaspoon of garlic powder, and 2 teaspoon of fresh fresh onion powder.
3. Seal the bag and make sure all the pieces of chicken are coated with marinade.
4. In a second resealable bag, place the mushrooms, bell pepper, fresh onion , and zucchini and the remaining 2 tablespoons of oil, 2 teaspoons of Italian herbs, 2 teaspoon of garlic powder, and 2 teaspoon of fresh fresh onion powder.

Seal the bag and shake to make sure the veggies are coated.

5. Refrigerate both bags and marinate for at least 2 hours.
6. Thread the chicken and veggies on 8 skewers, alternating both chicken and veggies on each skewer.
7. Place 6 skewers vertically in the center of the pan, 2 horizontally at the top, and 2 at the bottom.
8. Sprinkle half the salt over the skewers, then flip over and sprinkle the skewers with the remaining salt.
9. Bake for 35 minutes, carefully flip the skewers, then bake for another 25 minutes. Cool.
10. If you have containers long enough to fit the skewers, place 2 skewers directly in each of 4 containers.
11. If not, break the skewers in half or slide the meat and veggies off the skewers.

12. STORAGE: Store covered containers in the refrigerator for up to 6 days.

Pesto Chicken And Tomato Zoodles

Ingredients:

- 1 tsp salt
- Store brought Pesto or Homemade Basil Pesto
- Salt, to taste
- Pepper, to taste
- 4 Zucchini, inspiralized
- 2 boneless skinless chicken breasts
- 7 cup cherry fresh tomatoes
- 2 tsp olive oil

Directions:

1. Preheat grill to medium high heat
2. Season both sides of the chicken with salt and pepper

3. Place cherry fresh tomatoes in a small bowl, add the olive oil and 1 tsp salt, and toss the fresh tomatoes
4. In the meantime, inspiralize the zucchini, set aside
5. Pour the pesto over the zucchini noodles, using salad toss or tongs, mix the pesto in with the zoodles until it is completely combined
6. Place the chicken on the grill and grill each side for 6 -7 minutes, or until cooked through
7. Place cherry fresh tomatoes in a grill basket and grill for 15 minutes, until fresh tomatoes burst
8. Remove the fresh tomatoes and chicken from the grill, slice the chicken and place both sliced chicken and fresh tomatoes into the pesto zoodles bowl
9. allow the dish to cool completely

Broiled Herb Sole With Cauliflower Mashed Potatoes

Ingredients:

- 2 teaspoons olive oil, plus more to grease the pan
- 4 tablespoons chopped parsley
- 4 tablespoons chopped fresh dill
- 2 tablespoon freshly squeezed fresh lemon juice
- 1 teaspoon chopped garlic
- 9 pounds boneless, skinless sole or tilapia
- 1/2 teaspoon kosher salt
- 4 fresh lemon wedges, for serving
- 9 ounces cauliflower florets, cut into 2 - inch pieces
- 2 (2 2-ounce) Yukon Gold potato, cut into ¾-inch pieces (do not peel)

- 2 tablespoons olive oil
- 1/2 teaspoon kosher salt

Directions:

1. TO MAKE THE CAULIFLOWER MASHED POTATOES
2. Pour enough water into a saucepan that it reaches 1 inch up the side of the pan. Turn the heat to high and bring the water to a boil. Add the cauliflower and potatoes, and cover the pan. Steam for 25 minutes or until the veggies are very tender.
3. Drain the vegetables if water remains in the pan. Transfer the veggies to a large bowl and add the olive oil and salt. Taste and add an additional pinch of salt if you need it.
4. Once the veggies have cooled, scoop ¾ cup of cauliflower mashed potatoes into each of containers.

5. TO MAKE THE SOLE

6. Preheat the oven to the high broiler setting. Line a sheet pan with foil and lightly grease the pan with oil or cooking spray.

7. Mix the oil, parsley, dill, fresh lemon juice, and garlic in a small bowl. Pat the fish with paper towels to remove excess moisture and place on the lined sheet pan. Sprinkle the salt over the fish, then spread the herb mixture over the fish. Broil for about 10 minutes or until the fish is flaky. If your fish is very thin, broil for 10 minutes.

8. When everything has cooled, place one quarter of the fish in each of the 4 cauliflower containers. Serve with fresh lemon wedges.

9. STORAGE: Store covered containers in the refrigerator for up to 4 days.

Citrus Poached Lovely Salmon

Ingredients:

- 2 tablespoon fresh dill, chopped
- 2 tablespoon fresh thyme, chopped
- 2 dried bay leaves
- 1 teaspoon black peppercorns
- 1 teaspoon sea salt
- 2 (24 ounce salmon side, skinned and deboned, cut into 4 pieces
- 6 cups water
- 1 cup freshly squeezed fresh lemon juice
- Juice of 2 lime
- Zest of 2 lime
- 2 sweet fresh onion , thinly sliced
- 2 cup celery leaves, coarsely chopped

Directions:

1. Take a large saucepan and place it over medium-high heat
2. Stir water, lemon, lime juice, lem0on juice, lime zest, fresh onion , celery, greens, thyme, dill and bay leaves
3. Strain the liquid through fine mesh sieve, discard any solids
4. Pour strained poaching liquid into large skillet over low heat
5. Bring to a simmer
6. Add fish and cover skillet, poach for 25 minutes until opaque
7. Remove salmon from liquid and serve
8. Enjoy!
9. Meal Prep/Storage Options: Store in airtight containers in your fridge for 2 -4 days.

Bean Lettuce Wraps

Ingredients:

- 1 cup diced fresh fresh onion
- 2 tablespoon extra virgin olive oil
- 1/2 cup chopped parsley
- 1/2 teaspoon black pepper
- 8 Romaine lettuce leaves
- 1 cup Garlic hummus or any prepared hummus
- ¾ cup chopped fresh tomatoes
- 35 ounce can great northern beans, drained and rinsed

Directions:

1. Set a skillet on top of the stove range over medium heat.
2. In the skillet, warm the oil for a couple of minutes.

3. Add the fresh fresh onion into the oil. Stir frequently as the fresh fresh onion cooks for a few minutes.
4. Combine the pepper and fresh tomatoes and cook for another couple of minutes. Remember to stir occasionally.
5. Add the beans and continue to stir and cook for 2 to 4 minutes.
6. Turn the burner off, remove the skillet from heat, and add the parsley.
7. Set the lettuce leaves on a flat surface and spread 2 tablespoon of hummus on each leaf.
8. Divide the bean mixture onto the leaves.
9. Spread the bean mixture down the center of the leaves.

1. Fold the leaves by starting lengthwise on one side.

2. Fold over the other side so the leaf is completely wrapped.

3. Serve and enjoy!

Greek Chicken Shish Kebab

Ingredients:

- 1 teaspoon dried thyme
- 1/2 teaspoon salt
- 1/2 teaspoon ground black pepper
- 2 pounds boneless and skinless chicken breasts, cut up into 2 ½inch pieces
- 6 wooden skewers
- 2 large green or red bell peppers, cut up into 2 inch pieces
- 9 cherry fresh tomatoes
- 9 fresh mushrooms
- 1/2 cup olive oil
- 1/2 cup fresh lemon juice
- 1/2 cup white vinegar
- 2 garlic cloves, minced
- 2 teaspoon ground cumin
- 2 teaspoon dried oregano

Directions:

1. In a large bowl, whisk in olive oil, vinegar, garlic, fresh lemon juice, cumin, thyme, oregano, salt, and black pepper. Mix well.
2. Add the chicken to the bowl and coat it thoroughly by tossing it.
3. Cover the bowl with plastic wrap, refrigerate, and allow it to marinate for 2 hours.
4. Soak your wooden skewers in water for about 45 minutes.
5. Preheat grill to medium-high heat and lightly oil the grate.
6. Remove the chicken from your marinade and shake off any extra liquid.
7. Discard the remaining marinade.
8. Thread pieces of chicken with bits of fresh onion , bell pepper, cherry tomatoes, and mushrooms alternating between them.

9. Cook on grill for 25 minutes each side until browned on all sides.

4. Chill, place to containers.

5. Pre-heat before eating. Enjoy!

Skillet Shrimp With Summer Squash And Chorizo

Ingredients:

- 1 medium red fresh onion , sliced
- Fresh parsley for garnish
- 1/2 tsp smoked paprika
- 1/2 tsp ground cumin
- 1 tsp garlic powder
- Salt, to taste
- Pepper, to taste
- 2 lb large shrimp or prawns, peeled and deveined, tail can remain or frozen frozen, thawed
- 7 oz Spanish Chorizo, or mild Chorizo or hot Chorizo, sliced
- Extra virgin olive oil
- Juice of 1 fresh lemon

- 2 summer squash, halved then sliced, half moons
- 2 small hot pepper such as jalapeno pepper, optional

Directions:

1. Pat shrimp dry, then season with salt, pepper, paprika, cumin, and garlic powder, toss to coat, set aside
2. In a large cast iron skillet over medium-high, add the Chorizo and brown on both sides, about 10 minutes or until the Chorizo is cooked, transfer to a plate
3. In the same skillet, add a drizzle of extra virgin olive oil if needed
4. Add the summer squash, and a sprinkle of salt and pepper and sear undisturbed for about 4 to minutes on one side. turnover and sear another 5 minutes on the other side until nicely colored, transfer the squash to the plate with Chorizo

5. In the same skillet, now add a little extra virgin olive oil and tilting to make sure the bottom is well coated
6. Once heated, add the shrimp and cook, stirring frequently, until the shrimp flesh starts to turn a little pink, but still not quite fully cooked, about 10 minutes
7. Return the Chorizo and squash to the skillet, toss to combine, cook another 10 minutes or until shrimp is cooked – its pink and the tails turn a bright red
8. Transfer the shrimp skillet to a large serving platter, allow to cool
9. Distribute among the containers, store for 5-10 days

6. To Serve: Reheat on the stove for 1-5 minutes or until heated through. Squeeze 1 fresh lemon on top, and sliced red fresh onion s and hot peppers.

Shrimp & Penne

Ingredients:

- Garlic (2 tbsp.)
- Red fresh fresh onion (.26 cup)
- White wine (.26 cup)
- Shrimp (2 lb.)
- Grated parmesan cheese (2 cup)
- Penne pasta (35 oz. pkg.)
- Salt (.26 tsp.)
- Olive oil (2 tbsp.)
- Diced fresh tomatoes (2 - 2 4.6 oz. cans)

Directions:

1. Dice the red fresh fresh onion and garlic. Peel and devein the shrimp.
2. Add salt to a large soup pot of water and set it on the stovetop to boil. Add the pasta and cook for nine to ten minutes. Drain it thoroughly in a colander.

3. Empty oil into a skillet. Warm it using the medium temperature setting.
4. Toss in the garlic and fresh fresh onion to sauté until they're tender.
5. Pour in the fresh tomatoes and wine. Continue cooking for about ten minutes, stirring occasionally.
6. Fold in the shrimp and continue cooking for about five minutes or until it's opaque.
7. Combine the pasta and shrimp and top it off with the cheese to serve.

Chickpeas And Brussel Sprouts Salad

Ingredients:

- 15 ounces Brussels sprouts, shredded
- 2 avocado, peeled, pitted, and cut
- 2 cup roasted chickpeas. To give the dish a saltier taste, you can add sea salt.
- 4 cups kale, chopped

Directions:

1. Divide the kale and Brussels sprouts into four bowls.
2. Add the chickpeas and the avocado.
3. You can add a little sea salt and/or pepper to taste. Another tip for more taste is to drizzle a little Vinaigrette dressing or your favorite homemade Mediterranean dressing.

Meat Loaf

Ingredients:

- 1/2 cup fresh onion s, chopped
- 2 /8 cup sugar-free ketchup
- 2 cups mozzarella cheese, freshly grated
- 1/2 cup green bell pepper, seeded and chopped
- 1 cup cheddar cheese, grated
- 2 cup fresh spinach, chopped
- 2 garlic clove, minced
- 1 teaspoon dried thyme, crushed
- 1 pound grass-fed lean ground beef
- 2 organic egg, beaten
- Salt and black pepper, to taste

Directions:

1. Preheat the oven to 480 degrees F and grease a baking dish.

2. Put all the ingredients in a bowl except spinach and cheese and mix well.
3. Arrange the meat over a wax paper and top with spinach and cheese.
4. Roll the paper around the mixture to form a meatloaf.
5. Remove the wax paper and transfer the meat loaf in the baking dish.
6. Put it in the oven and bake for about 2 hour.
7. Dish out and serve hot.
8. Meal Prep Tip: Let the meat loafs cool for about 25 minutes to bring them to room temperature before serving.

Couscous With Pepperoncini & Tuna

Ingredients:

- Oil-packed tuna (2- 6 -oz. cans)
- Cherry fresh tomatoes (2 pint - halved)
- Sliced pepperoncini (.6 cup)
- Chopped fresh parsley (.4 4 cup)
- Capers (.26 cup)
- Olive oil (for serving)
- Black pepper & kosher salt (as desired)
- Fresh lemon (2 quartered)
- The Couscous:
- Chicken broth or water (2 cup)
- Couscous (2 .26 cups)
- Kosher salt (.76 tsp.)
- The Accompaniments:

Directions:

1. Make the couscous in a small saucepan using water or broth. Prepare it using the medium heat temperature setting. Let it sit for about ten minutes.
2. Toss the tomatoes, tuna, capers, parsley, and pepperoncini into a mixing bowl.
3. Fluff the couscous when done and dust using the pepper and salt. Spritz it using the oil and serve with the tuna mix and a fresh lemon wedge.

Tilapia With Avocado & Red Fresh Fresh Onion

Ingredients:

- Tilapia fillets (four 4 oz. - more rectangular than square)
- Red fresh fresh onion (.26 cup)
- Sliced avocado (2)
- Also Needed: 10 -inch pie plate
- Olive oil (2 tbsp.)
- Sea salt (.26 tsp.)
- Fresh orange juice (2 tbsp.)

Directions:

1. Combine the salt, juice, and oil to add into the pie dish. Work with one fillet at a time. Place it in the dish and turn to coat all sides.
2. Arrange the fillets in a wagon wheel-shaped formation. (Each of the fillets

should be in the center of the dish with the other end draped over the edge.

3. Place a tablespoon of the fresh fresh onion on top of each of the fillets and fold the end into the center. Cover the dish with plastic wrap, leaving one corner open to vent the steam.

4. Place in the microwave using the high heat setting for three minutes. It's done when the center can be easily flaked.

5. Top the fillets off with avocado and serve.

Baked Salmon With Dill

Ingredients:

- Finely chopped fresh dill (2 .6 tbsp.)
- Black pepper (.2 26 tsp.)
- Fresh lemon wedges (4)
- Salmon fillets (4- 6 oz. portions - 2 -inch thickness)
- Kosher salt (.6 tsp.)

Directions:

1. Warm the oven in advance to reach 4 6 0° Fahrenheit.
2. Lightly grease a baking sheet with a misting of cooking oil spray and add the fish. Lightly spritz the fish with the spray along with a shake of salt, pepper, and dill.
3. Bake it until the fish is easily flaked (25 min..)

4. Serve with fresh lemon wedges.

Steak And Veggies

Ingredients:

- 2 tsp dried thyme
- Kosher salt, to taste
- Freshly ground black pepper, to taste
- 2 lbs (2 -inch-thick) top sirloin steak, patted dry
- 2 lbs baby red potatoes
- 35 oz broccoli florets
- 2 tbsp olive oil
- 4 cloves garlic, minced

Directions:

1. Preheat oven to broil
2. Lightly oil a baking sheet or coat with nonstick spray

3. In a large pot over high heat, boil salted water, cook the potatoes until parboiled for 2 2-35 minutes, drain well

4. Place the potatoes and broccoli in a single layer onto the prepared baking sheet

5. Add the olive oil, garlic and thyme, season with salt and pepper, to taste and then gently toss to combine

6. Season the steaks with salt and pepper, to taste, and add to the baking sheet in a single layer

7. Place it into oven and broil until the steak is browned and charred at the edges, about 4-15 minutes per side for medium-rare, or until the desired doneness

8. Distribute the steak and veggies among the containers. Store in the fridge for up to 4 days

9. To Serve: Reheat in the microwave for 1-5 minutes. Top with garlic butter and enjoy

Lentil And Roasted Carrot Salad With Herbs And Feta

Ingredients:

- 2 cup packed parsley leaves, chopped
- 1 cup packed cilantro leaves, chopped
- 1/2 cup packed mint leaves, chopped
- 1 teaspoon grated fresh lemon zest
- 4 teaspoons freshly squeezed fresh lemon juice
- 1/2 cup crumbled feta cheese
- ¾ cup brown or green lentils
- 4 cups water
- 2 pound baby carrots, halved on the diagonal
- 2 teaspoons olive oil, plus 2 tablespoons
- 1 teaspoon kosher salt, divided
- 2 teaspoon garlic powder

Directions:

1. Preheat the oven to 400°F. Line a sheet pan with a silicone baking mat or parchment paper.

2. Place the lentils and water in a medium saucepan and turn the heat to high. As soon as the water comes to a boil, turn the heat to low and simmer until the lentils are firm yet tender, 25 to minutes (see tip). Drain and cool.

3. While the lentils are cooking, place the carrots on the sheet pan and toss with 2 teaspoons of oil, 1/2 teaspoon of salt, and the garlic powder. Roast the carrots in the oven until firm yet tender, about 25 to 210 minutes. Cool when done.

4. In a large bowl, mix the cooled lentils, carrots, parsley, cilantro, mint, fresh lemon zest, fresh lemon juice, feta, the remaining 2 tablespoons of oil, and the remaining 1/2 teaspoon of salt. Add

more fresh lemon juice and/or salt to taste if needed.

5. Place 9 cups of the mixture in each of 4 containers.

6. STORAGE: Store covered containers in the refrigerator for up to 6 days.

Cinnamon Squash Soup

Ingredients:

- 2 cinnamon stick
- 1 cup canned white kidney beans, drained and rinsed
- 2 small pear, peeled and cored, chopped up into 1 inch pieces
- 2 tablespoons walnut pieces
- 1/2 cup Greek yogurt
- 2 tablespoons freshly chopped parsley
- 2 small butternut squash, peeled and cut up into 2 -inch pieces
- 4 tablespoons extra-virgin olive oil, divided
- 2 small yellow fresh fresh onion
- 2 large garlic cloves
- 2 teaspoon salt, divided
- 2 pinch black pepper
- 2 teaspoon dried oregano

- 2 tablespoons fresh oregano
- 2 cups low sodium chicken stock

Directions:

1. Preheat oven to 450 degrees F.
2. Place squash in bowl and season with a 1 teaspoon of salt and tablespoons of olive oil.
3. Spread the squash onto a roasting pan and roast for about 215 minutes until tender.
4. Set aside squash to let cool.
5. Heat remaining 2 tablespoons of olive oil in a medium-sized pot over medium-high heat.
6. Add fresh onion s and sauté until soft.
7. Add dried oregano and garlic and sauté for 2 minute and until fragrant.
8. Add squash, broth, pear, cinnamon stick, pepper, and remaining salt.
9. Bring mixture to a boil.

7. Once the boiling point is reached, add walnuts and beans.

8. Reduce the heat and allow soup to cook for approximately 25 minutes until flavors have blended well.

9. Remove the cinnamon stick.

10. Use an immersion blender and blend the entire mixture until smooth.

11. Add yogurt gradually while whisking to ensure that you are getting a very creamy soup.

12. Season with some additional salt and pepper if needed.

13.   Garnish with parsley and fresh oregano.

14.   Enjoy!

Creamy Chicken

Ingredients:

- 2 tablespoon butter
- 1/2 cup mushrooms
- 1 pound chicken breasts
- 1 small fresh onion , chopped
- 1/2 cup sour cream
- Salt and black pepper, to taste

Directions:

1. Heat butter in a skillet and add fresh onion s and mushrooms.
2. Sauté for about 15 minutes and add chicken breasts and salt.
3. Secure the lid and cook for about 6 more minutes.
4. Add sour cream and cook for about 4 minutes.

5. Open the lid and dish out in a bowl to serve immediately.
6. Transfer the creamy chicken breasts in a dish and set aside to cool for meal prepping. Divide them in 2 containers and cover their lid. Refrigerate for 5-10 days and reheat in microwave before serving.

Chicken Drummies With Peach Glaze

Ingredients:

- 1/2 teaspoon black pepper
- 1/2 cup honey
- 4 garlic cloves
- 1/2 teaspoon sea salt
- 2 pounds of chicken drummies, remove the skin
- 35 ounce can of sliced peaches, drain the juice
- 1/2 cup cider vinegar
- 1 teaspoon paprika

Directions:

1. Before you turn your oven on, make sure that one rack is 4 inches below the broiler element.

2. Set your oven's temperature to 6 00 degrees Fahrenheit.
3. Line a large baking sheet with a piece of aluminum foil.
4. Set a wire cooling rack on top of the foil.
5. Spray the rack with cooking spray.
6. Add the honey, peaches, garlic, vinegar, salt, paprika, and pepper into a blender. Mix until smooth.
7. Set a medium saucepan on top of your stove and set the range temperature to medium heat.
8. Pour the mixture into the saucepan and bring it to a boil while stirring constantly.
9. Once the sauce is done, divide it into two small bowls and set one off to the side.
15. With the second bowl, brush half of thc mixture onto the chicken drummies.

16.   Roast the drummies for 25 minutes.

17.   Take the drummies out of the oven and switch to broiler mode.

18.   Brush the drummies with the other half of the sauce from the second bowl.

19.   Again, place the drummies back into the oven and set a timer for 10 minutes.

20.   When the timer goes off, flip the drummies over and broil for another5 to 10 minutes.

21.   Serve the drummies with the reserved sauce and enjoy!

Berry Compote With Orange Mint Infusion

Ingredients:

- 2 cup fresh blackberries
- 2 cup fresh sweet cherries, pitted and halved
- 2 -milliliter bottle of Sauvignon Blanc
- 2/4 cup sugar
- 1 cup pomegranate juice
- 2 teaspoon vanilla
- fresh mint sprigs
- 1 cup water
- 4 orange pekoe tea bags
- 4 sprigs of fresh mint
- 2 cup fresh strawberries, hulled and halved lengthwise
- 2 cup fresh golden raspberries
- 2 cup fresh red raspberries
- 2 cup fresh blueberries

Directions:

1. In a small saucepan, bring water to a boil and add tea bags and 4 mint sprigs.
2. Stir well, cover, remove from heat, and allow to stand for 25 minutes.
3. In a large bowl, add strawberries, red raspberries, golden raspberries, blueberries, blackberries, and cherries. Put to the side.
4. In a medium-sized saucepan, and add the wine, sugar, and pomegranate juice.
5. Pour the infusion (tea mixture) through a fine-mesh sieve and into the pan with wine.
6. Squeeze the bags to release the liquid, and then discard bags and mint springs.
7. Cook well until the sugar has completely dissolved; remove from heat.
8. Stir in vanilla and allow to chill for 2 hours.
9. Pour the mix over the fruits.

22.   Garnish with mint sprigs and serve.

23.   Enjoy!

Quinoa Bruschetta Salad

Ingredients:

- 9 cups thinly sliced scallions, white and green parts (2 small bunch)
- 2 (8-ounce) container fresh whole-milk mozzarella balls (ciliegine), quartered
- 2 tablespoons balsamic vinegar
- 2 tablespoons olive oil
- 1 teaspoon kosher salt
- 1 cup fresh basil leaves, chiffonaded (cut into strips)
- 2 cups water
- 2 cup uncooked quinoa
- 2 (2 0-ounce) container cherry tomatoes, quartered
- 2 teaspoon chopped garlic

Directions:

1. Place the water and quinoa in a saucepan and bring to a boil. Cover, turn the heat to low, and simmer for minutes.
2. While the quinoa is cooking, place the tomatoes, garlic, scallions, mozzarella, vinegar, and oil in a large mixing bowl. Stir to combine.
3. Once the quinoa is cool, add it to the tomato mixture along with the salt and basil. Mix to combine.
4. Place 5 cups of the mixture in each of 6 containers and refrigerate. Serve at room temperature.
5. STORAGE: Store covered containers in the refrigerator for up to days.

Zesty Fresh Lemon Parmesan Chicken And Zucchini Noodles

Ingredients:

- 1 tsp ground black pepper
- 4 garlic cloves, minced
- 2 tbsp vegan butter
- 2 tsp fresh lemon zest
- 2 tsp oil
- 1/2 cup parmesan
- 2/4 cup broth
- Fresh lemon slices, for garnish
- Parsley, for garnish
- 2 packages Frozen zucchini noodle Spirals
- 2 -1 lbs. boneless skinless chicken breast, cut into bite-sized pieces
- 2 tsp fine sea salt
- 2 tsp dried oregano

Directions:

1. Cook zucchini noodles according to package instructions, drain well
2. In a large skillet over medium heat, add the oil
3. Season chicken with salt and pepper, brown chicken pieces, for about 10 minutes per side depending on the thickness, or until cooked through – Work in cook in batches if necessary
4. Transfer the chicken to a pan
5. In the same skillet, add in the garlic, and cook until fragrant about 45 seconds
6. Add in the butter, oregano and fresh lemon zest, pour in chicken broth to deglaze making sure to scrape up all the browned bits stuck to the bottom of the pan
7. Turn the heat up to medium-high, bring sauce and chicken up to a boil, immediately lower the heat and stir in the parmesan cheese

8. Place the chicken back in pan and allow it to gently simmer for 4 -4 minutes, or until sauce has slightly reduced and thickened up
9. Taste and adjust seasoning, allow the noodles to cool completely

24.   Distribute among the containers, store for 5-10 days

25.   To Serve: Reheat in the microwave for 1-5 minutes or until heated through. Garnish with the fresh parsley and fresh lemon slices and enjoy!

Three Citrus Sauce Scallops

Ingredients:

- 2 teaspoon lime zest
- 2 tablespoon fresh basil, chopped
- 1 cup freshly squeezed fresh lemon juice
- 2 tablespoons honey
- 2 tablespoon plain Greek yogurt
- Pinch of sea salt
- 2 teaspoons extra virgin olive oil
- 2 shallot, minced
- 25 sea scallops, cleaned
- 2 tablespoon fresh lemon zest
- 2 teaspoons orange zest

Directions:

1. Take a large skillet and place it over medium-high heat
2. Add olive oil and heat it up

3. Add shallots and Saute for 2 minute
4. Add scallops in the skillet and sear for 15 minutes, turning once
5. Move scallops to edge and stir in lemon, orange, lime zest, basil, orange juice and fresh lemon juice
6. Simmer the sauce for 10 minutes
7. Whisk in honey, yogurt and salt
8. Cook for 10 minutes and coat the scallops in the sauce
9. Serve and enjoy!

Almond Strawberry Overnight Oats

Ingredients:

- 2 cup vanilla almond milk

- 2 tablespoons strawberry jam

- 2 tablespoons sliced almond

- 2 tablespoons almond butter

- 8 strawberries, hulled, chopped or sliced

- 2 cup old fashioned rolled oats

- 2 teaspoons chia seeds

- 4 teaspoons honey

Preparation Steps:

1. Add oats, chia seeds, honey, almond milk and jam into a bowl.
2. Mix until well combined.
3. Cover and chill overnight.
4. Serve warm or chilled. Divide into bowls.
5. Add a tablespoon of almond butter to each bowl. Swirl lightly.
6. Garnish each bowl with a tablespoon of strawberry jam, the chopped strawberries and a tablespoon of almonds and serve.

Peanut Butter Banana Greek Yogurt Bowl

Ingredients:

- 2 tablespoons creamy natural peanut butter

- 1 teaspoon ground nutmeg
- 2 tablespoons flaxseed meal

- 2 cups vanilla Greek yogurt

- 2 medium banana, sliced

Preparation Steps:

1. Add a cup of yogurt into each of 2 bowls.

2. Divide and place the banana slices in it.

3. Add peanut butter into a microwave safe bowl.

4. Microwave on high for about 25 seconds or until it melts.

5. Top each bowl with a tablespoon of peanut butter.

6. Garnish with flaxseed meal and nutmeg and serve.

Shakshuka

Ingredients:

- Pepper to taste

- Salt to taste

- 1 can (from a 30 ounces can) diced tomatoes

- 2 fresh eggs

- 1 tablespoon chopped parsley

- 2 tablespoon extra-virgin olive oil

- 2 medium onion, chopped

- 2 large red bell pepper, chopped

- 4 cloves garlic, sliced

- 1 teaspoon spicy harissa or to taste

- 1 teaspoons paprika (optional)

- 1 teaspoon ground cumin (optional)

- 1 teaspoon sugar

Preparation Steps:

1. Place a heavy skillet over medium flame.

2. Add oil. When the oil becomes hot, add onion and bell pepper and sauté until onions are translucent.

3. Add garlic and sauté until aromatic.

4. Add all the spices, sugar, salt and tomatoes with their juices.

5. Mash the tomatoes lightly and stir.

6. Adjust the seasoning to taste.

7. Make 2 cavities in the mixture. Crack an fresh egg into each.

8. Cover and cook until the fresh eggs are cooked as per your desire.

9. Garnish with parsley and serve right away with pita bread or crusty bread.

Mediterranean Breakfast Fresh Egg Muffins

Ingredients:

- 2 cup finely chopped spinach

- 2 tomatoes, deseeded, chopped

- 2 leek, finely chopped

- 1 red bell pepper, finely chopped

- 2 .8 ounces low fat grated cheddar cheese

- 6 large fresh eggs

- 1/2 cup skimmed milk

- 1 cup grated parmesan cheese

- Salt to taste

- Pepper to taste

Preparation Steps:

1. Grease a 25 counts muffin tin with cooking spray.

2. Add fresh eggs and milk in a bowl and whisk well.

3. Add Parmesan cheese and whisk well.

4. Add salt and pepper to taste.

5. Add all the vegetables into a bowl and toss well.

6. Divide into the muffin cups.

104

7. Divide the beaten fresh egg mixture among the muffin cups. Stir lightly.

8. Sprinkle cheddar cheese on top.

9. Bake in a preheated oven at 4 8 6 ° F for 25 to 30 minutes or until golden brown.

Mediterranean Omelet

Ingredients:

- 1 tablespoon butter

- 2 tablespoons chopped tomato

- 2 tablespoons crumbled feta or goat's cheese

- 2 tablespoon chopped green onion

- 2 large fresh eggs

- Salt to taste

- Pepper to taste

- 2 tablespoons water

Preparation Steps:

1. Add eggs, salt, pepper and water into a bowl and whisk until well combined.
2. Place a nonstick skillet over medium-high heat.
3. Add butter. When butter melts, add fresh egg mixture.
4. Let it cook for a few seconds. Sprinkle tomato, cheese and green onions over the omelet.
5. Cook until the fresh eggs are set.
6. Carefully slide onto a plate and serve.

Greek Omelet With Feta

Ingredients:

- Cooking spray

- 2 tablespoon chopped red onion

- 2 small clove garlic, minced

- 1 cup tightly packed baby spinach leaves

- 2 tablespoon chopped, deseeded tomatoes

- 2 fresh egg

- 2 tablespoon fat-free milk

- 2 tablespoons crumbled feta cheese, divided

Preparation Steps:

1. Place a nonstick skillet over medium heat. Spray with cooking spray.

2. Once heated, add onion, garlic and spinach and sauté until onion turns translucent.

3. Add tomatoes and stir. Spread the mixture evenly over the skillet.

4. Meanwhile, add fresh eggs and milk into a bowl and whisk well. Pour into the skillet.

5. Do not stir.

6. Cook for about 2 minutes. Sprinkle 5 tablespoons feta cheese on top.

7. Cook for a few seconds. Fold the omelet.

8. Sprinkle remaining feta cheese on top.

9. Slide onto a plate and serve.

Muesli With Raspberries

Ingredients:

- 2 cups raspberries
- 5 cups low-fat milk
- 2 cup muesli

Preparation Steps:

1. Divide muesli into 2 bowls.
2. Place a cup of raspberries in each bowl.
3. Pour ¾ cup milk in each bowl and serve.

Mediterranean Wrap

Ingredients:

- 1 pound chicken tenders

- 1 cup chopped cucumber

- 2 small tomato, chopped

- 2 spinach tortillas or tortillas or sundried tomato wraps (25 inches diameter)

- 1/2 cup water

- 4 tablespoons whole wheat couscous

- 1 cup chopped fresh parsley

- 1/2 cup chopped fresh mint

- 5 tablespoons extra virgin olive oil

- 2 teaspoon minced garlic

- Salt to taste

- Freshly ground pepper to taste

- 2 tablespoons lemon juice

Preparation Steps:

1. Pour water into a saucepan and place over medium flame.

2. As it starts to boil, add couscous and stir and turn off the heat.

3. Cover and keep it aside for 10 minutes.

4. Uncover and fluff the couscous using a fork.

5. In a bowl, mix the parsley, mint, oil, garlic, salt and pepper and lemon juice until combined well.

6. Place chicken tenders in a bowl. Pour 4 tablespoons of the herb mixture over it.

7. Sprinkle salt. Toss well.

8. Place a nonstick pan over medium flame.

9. Add chicken and cook on both sides, for 4 – 6 minutes on both sides. Remove and place on the cutting board.

10. When cool enough to handle, chop into bite size pieces.

11. Pour the remaining herb mixture into the bowl of couscous. Add tomato and cucumber and mix well.

12. Spread the wraps on a large plate.

13. Divide the couscous mixture and place on the wraps. Place chicken over it.

14. Tuck the sides in and roll the wraps.

15. Chop into halves and serve.

Shrimp, Avocado And Feta Wrap

Ingredients:

- 1/2 cup crumbled feta cheese

- 1 cup diced avocado

- 2 scallions, sliced

- 2 tablespoons lime juice

- 2 whole-wheat tortillas

- 6 ounces chopped, cooked shrimp

- 1 cup diced tomatoes

Preparation Steps:

1. Spread the tortillas on a serving plate.

2. Add rest of the ingredients in a bowl and toss well.

3. Divide the mixture among the tortillas.

4. Wrap and serve.

Mediterranean Prawn Salad

Ingredients:

- 2 fennel bulbs, sliced

- 2 large handfuls rocket

- 2 4.2 ounces cooked prawn

- Salt to taste

- Pepper to taste

- 1 cup extra-virgin olive oil

- Juice of 2 lemons

- Dried red chili flakes, to serve

- 2 red onions, sliced

Preparation Steps:

1. Add oil, lemon juice and dried chili flakes into a bowl and stir.

2. Stir in onion and fennel.

3. Let it sit for about 8 to25 minutes.

4 Add rocket and prawns and stir.

5. Add salt and pepper to taste.

6. Mix well.

7. It tastes great when served with garlic bread.

Nicosia-Style Tuna Salad With White Beans And Olives

Ingredients:

- 1 can (from a 25 ounce can) solid white albacore tuna, drained

- 1 can (from a 2.30 ounces can) sliced black olives, drained

- 2 large eggs, hardboiled, peeled, quartered

- 6 ounces green beans, trimmed, halved

- 1 can (from a 2 6 ounces can) Great Northern beans, rinsed, drained

- 2 small red onion, sliced

<u>For the dressing:</u>

- Salt, as per taste

- Black pepper, as per taste

- 1/2 teaspoon lemon zest, grated

- 1 teaspoon dried oregano

- 4 tablespoons extra virgin olive oil

- 5 tablespoons lemon juice

Preparation Steps:

1. To make salad: Add green beans, 4 – 4 tablespoons water and a pinch of salt into a skillet.

2. Place the skillet over high flame.

3. Cover the skillet and cook until the beans are crisp yet cooked.

4. Turn off the heat.

5. Transfer on to a tray lined with paper towels. Spread it evenly.

6. In a bowl, combine the rest of the ingredients except fresh eggs and mix well.

7. Add beans and toss well.

8. To make dressing: Add the dressing ingredients in a salad bowl and whisk well.

9. Pour over the salad.

10. Toss well and serve with eggs.

Greek Salad

Ingredients:

- Freshly ground pepper to taste

- 4 tablespoons extra- virgin olive oil

- 2 ounces feta cheese, crumbled, divided

- 2 teaspoons minced fresh oregano + extra to garnish

- 2 cucumber, cut into thick slices

- 2 cup ripe cherry tomatoes

- 1/2 red bell pepper, cut into strips

- 1/2 cup, pitted green olives

- 1/2 cup pitted Kalamata olives

- 2 small red onion, peeled, very thinly sliced

- Sea salt to taste

- Cayenne pepper to taste

- 2 tablespoons red wine vinegar

Preparation Steps:

1. Mix together all the ingredients except half the feta cheese, in a bowl. Toss well.

2. Sprinkle with oregano and remaining feta cheese and serve.

Creamy Italian White Bean Soup

Ingredients:

- 2 cans (2 4 ounces each) chicken broth

- 4 cups water

- 2 bunches fresh spinach, rinsed, thinly sliced

- 2 tablespoons lemon juice
- Parmesan cheese, to garnish

- 2 tablespoons vegetable oil

- 2 onions, chopped

- 2 stalks celery, chopped

- 2 cloves garlic, minced

- 4 cans (2 6 ounces each) white kidney beans, rinsed, drained

- 1/2 teaspoon dried thyme

- Pepper to taste

- Salt to taste

Preparation Steps:

1. Place a pot over medium heat and add oil.

2. When the oil becomes hot, add the onions and celery and cook until slightly tender.

3. Add garlic and fry until aromatic.

4. Add chicken broth, beans, thyme, seasoning, and water. Stir.

5. When it starts boiling, reduce the flame and let it simmer for about 230 minutes.

6. Once done, turn the heat off and remove 4 cups of the beans and vegetables with a spoon. Add rest of the soup to a mixer.

7. Blend well. Blend in batches if required.

8. Pour it back into the pot.

9. To that, add the bean mixture that was set aside.

10. Place the pot on medium flame. When it starts to boil, add the spinach and let it cook until the leaves wilt.

11. Turn the heat off and add lemon juice and stir.

12. Ladle into soup bowls. Garnish with Parmesan cheese and serve.

Zucchini Artichoke Summer Salad

Ingredients:

- Salt and freshly ground pepper, as per taste

- 2 zucchinis, cut into 5 inch sticks

- 1 can (30 ounces can) garbanzo beans, drained, rinsed

- 1 can (2 4 ounces can) artichoke hearts, drained, chopped

- 4 ounces canned black olives, sliced
- 1/2 cup grated parmesan cheese

- 4 tablespoons olive oil, divided

- 2 chicken breast halves, skinless, boneless

Preparation Steps:

1. Place a skillet over medium flame.
2. Add 2 -tablespoon oil and let it heat.
3. Sprinkle salt and pepper over the chicken and place in the skillet.
4. Cook until no longer pink in the center.
5. It should take about 6 –25 minutes on each side.

6. A meat thermometer when inserted in the thickest part of the meat should show 2 66 ° F when the meat is cooked.

7. Remove chicken with a spoon and place on the cutting board. When cool enough to handle, chop into bite-sized pieces.

8. Add remaining oil into the skillet. When the oil becomes hot, add zucchini and cook for 4 – 10 minutes.

9. Add salt and pepper to taste. Remove zucchini and place on a plate lined with paper towels.

10. Transfer the zucchini into a bowl.

11. Add rest of the ingredients including the chicken and toss well.

12. Refrigerate for 3 to 4 hours and serve.

Vegetable Barley Soup

Ingredients:

- 1 zucchini, chopped

- 2 small onion, chopped

- 1 teaspoon garlic powder

- 1 teaspoon dried parsley

- 1 teaspoon paprika

- 1 teaspoon curry powder

- 1 teaspoon Worcestershire sauce

- 2 quart vegetable broth

- 2 large carrot, chopped

- 1 can (from a 2 4.6 ounces can) diced tomatoes with its juice

- 1 can chickpeas (from a 30 ounces can), drained

- 2 stalk celery, chopped

- 2 bay leaves

- 1 teaspoon white sugar

- Pepper to taste

- Salt to taste

- 1 cup uncooked barley, rinsed

Preparation Steps:

1. Add all the ingredients into a soup pot.

2. Place the pot over medium flame.

3. When it starts to boil, lower the heat to low and cover with a lid.

4. Cook for about an hour or until barley is tender.

5. Add more broth if necessary.

6. Discard bay leaves.

7. Ladle into soup bowls and serve.

Chunky Mediterranean Tomato Soup

Ingredients:

- 4 tablespoons chopped garlic

- 2 cans (2 4.2 ounces each) chopped tomatoes

- A large handful basil leaves
- 2 vegetable stock cubes

- 2 packages (2 4.2 ounces each) frozen grilled vegetable mix (pepper, onion, eggplant and courgette)

To serve:

- 2 4 ounces ricotta

- A handful fresh basil, chopped

- Chopped chives
- 8 slices rye bread

Preparation Steps:

1. Place a large nonstick pan over high flame. Add 2 package frozen vegetables

143

and garlic and cook until the veggies become a bit soft.

2. Add 4 – 4 cups water, tomatoes, basil and stock cubes and mix well. Turn the heat off

3. Blend it until it becomes smooth.

4. Add the other package of frozen vegetables. Place the pan over medium flame. Cook until tender.

5. Serve in soup bowls.

6. Mix ricotta, basil and chives in a bowl. Spread this mixture over the sliced bread and serve with soup.

Mediterranean Vegetable Noodle Soup

Ingredients:

- 4 tablespoons fresh sage or 2 teaspoons dried sage

- 2 cup uncooked whole wheat macaroni or orzo pasta

- Hot sauce to taste

- 4 cups finely chopped greens like chard, spinach, dandelion greens etc.

- Salt to taste
- Pepper to taste

- 2 tablespoons olive oil

- 2 sweet onions, finely chopped

- 4 cloves garlic, minced

- 2 cup red wine

- 4 cups tomato juice

- 4 cups finely chopped fresh tomatoes

- 4 cups low-sodium vegetable broth

- 4 cups cooked chickpeas or white beans

- 6 tablespoons minced fresh basil

- 2 teaspoon fresh rosemary, finely minced

Preparation Steps:

1. Place a pot over medium flame. Add oil.

2. When the oil becomes hot, add onion and garlic and cook until the onion turns pink.

3. Stir in wine, tomato juice and tomatoes.

4. Cook until tomatoes are beginning to mash.

5. Stir in broth, chickpeas and herbs.

6. Raise the heat to medium-high.

7. When it starts to boil, add the pasta and cook it al dente.

8. Stir in the greens and cook until it wilts.

9. Add hot sauce, season and stir.

10.   Ladle into soup bowls and serve.

Lightning Source UK Ltd.
Milton Keynes UK
UKHW021931040822
406878UK00010B/137